CW00521253

Maths

Assessment Papers

8-9 years

OXFORD

UNIVERSITY PRESS

OXFORD
UNIVERSITY PRESS

Great Clarendon Street, Oxford, OX2 6DP, United Kingdom

Oxford University Press is a department of the University of Oxford.
It furthers the University's objective of excellence in research, scholarship,
and education by publishing worldwide. Oxford is a registered trade mark of
Oxford University Press in the UK and in certain other countries

British Library Cataloguing in Publication Data
Data available

978-0-19-274013-7

20 19 18 17 16 15 14 13 12

Paper used in the production of this book is a natural, recyclable
product made from wood grown in sustainable forests.
The manufacturing process conforms to the environmental
regulations of the country of origin.

Printed in Poland by Opolgraf SA

Acknowledgements

The publishers would like to thank the following for permissions to
use copyright material:

Page make-up: OKS Prepress, India
Illustrations: Tech-Set Limited
Cover illustrations: Lo Cole

Although we have made every effort to trace and contact all
copyright holders before publication this has not been possible in all
cases. If notified, the publisher will rectify any errors or omissions at
the earliest opportunity.

Links to third party websites are provided by Oxford in good faith
and for information only. Oxford disclaims any responsibility for
the materials contained in any third party website referenced in
this work.

Before you get started

What is Bond?

This book is part of the Bond Assessment Papers series for maths, which provides **thorough and continuous practice of all the key maths content** from ages five to thirteen. Bond's maths resources are ideal preparation for many different kinds of tests and exams – from SATs to 11+ and other secondary school selection exams.

What does this book cover?

It covers all the maths that a child of this age would be expected to learn and is fully in line with the National Curriculum for maths and the National Numeracy Strategy. One of the key features of Bond Assessment Papers is that each one practises **a wide variety of skills and question types** so that children are always challenged to think – and don't get bored repeating the same question type again and again. We think that variety is the key to effective learning. It helps children 'think on their feet' and cope with the unexpected.

The age given on the cover is for guidance only. As the papers are designed to be reasonably challenging for the age group, any one child may naturally find him or herself working above or below the stated age. The important thing is that children are always encouraged by their performance. Working at the right level is the key to this.

What does the book contain?

- **24 papers** – each one contains 40 questions.
- **Scoring devices** – there are score boxes in the margins and a Progress Chart on page 64. The chart is a visual and motivating way for children to see how they are doing. Encouraging them to colour in the chart as they go along and to try to beat their last score can be highly effective!
- **Next Steps** – advice on what to do after finishing the papers can be found on the inside back cover.
- **Answers** – located in an easily-removed central pull-out section.
- **Key maths words** – on page 1 you will find a glossary of special key words that are used in the papers. These are highlighted in bold each time that they appear. These words are now used in the maths curriculum and children are expected to know them at this age.

How can you use this book?

One of the great strengths of Bond Assessment Papers is their flexibility. They can be used at home, school and by tutors to:

- provide regular maths practice in **bite-sized chunks**
- **highlight strengths and weaknesses** in the core skills

- identify **individual needs**
- set **homework**
- set **timed formal practice** tests – allow about 30 minutes.

It is best to start at the beginning and work though the papers in order.

What does a score mean and how can it be improved?

If children colour in the Progress Chart at the back, this will give you an idea of how they are doing. The Next Steps inside the back cover will help you to decide what to do next to help a child progress. We suggest that it is always valuable to go over any wrong answers with children.

Don't forget the website ...!

Visit www.bond11plus.co.uk for lots of advice, information and suggestions on everything to do with Bond, exams, and helping children to do their best.

Key words

Some special maths words are used in this book. You will find them in **bold** each time they appear in the papers. These words are explained here.

area
the space inside a shape. Area is measured in square units, for example square centimetres (cm^2) or square metres (m^2)

cube
a solid shape whose faces are all squares, such as a child's building block

cuboid
a solid shape whose faces are either all rectangles, or rectangles and squares such as a cereal packet

digit
any single number, for example 4 has one digit, 37 has two digits, 437 has three digits

divisible
can be divided by, for example 4 is divisible by 2

equilateral triangle
a triangle which has all its sides of the same length

faces
flat sides of a solid object

heptagon
a shape with seven sides

hexagon
a shape with six sides

isosceles triangle
a triangle which has two sides the same length

mirror line
the line in which a shape can be reflected, like the reflection in a mirror

multiple
a number which another number multiplies into, for example 3, 6, 9, 12, 15, 60, 93 are multiples of 3

net
the flat shape that a three-dimensional object, such as a box, will make if you open it out

octagon
a shape with 8 sides

parallelogram
a four-sided shape that has its opposite sides parallel

pentagon
a shape with five sides

perimeter
the distance round the outside of a shape

pictogram
a diagram that records something using pictures

polygon
a shape with three or more sides

product
the answer when you multiply two numbers together, for example the product of 4 and 2 is 8

quadrilateral
a shape with 4 sides

round
means roughly or approximately, for example 42 rounded to the nearest 10 is 40, 470 rounded to the nearest 100 is 500

semicircle
a shape which is half a circle

square
a square is a rectangle with four equal sides

sum
the answer when you add two numbers together. The sum of 2 and 4 is 6

symmetry
if a shape has symmetry it has one or more mirror lines like this:

tetrahedron
a solid shape with four triangular faces

Venn diagram
a chart for sorting information of different kinds

The area of this square ☐ = 1, what is the area of each of the shapes below?

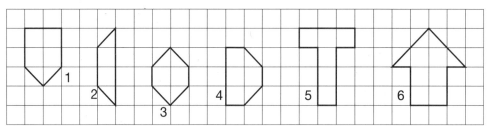

1 $=5$ ✓

2 $=3$ ✓

3 $=4$ ✓

4 $=5$ ✓

5 $=6$ ✓

6 $=8$ ✓

⑥ 6

7 Rachel is twice as old as Amy. If Amy is 7, how old is Rachel?

14 ✓

① 1

8 How many faces does this **cube** have?

6 ✓

9 Underline the correct answer. Each face on the **cube** is:

a triangle   <u>a square</u> ✓   a circle   a rectangle

10 How many **faces** does this **cuboid** have?

6 ✓

11 Underline the correct answer. Each face on the **cuboid** is:

a triangle   <u>a square</u>   a circle   <u>a rectangle</u> ✓

④ 4

2

There are 60 minutes in an hour. How many minutes are there between:

12 (06:19) and (06:30)   11 ✓

13 (02:27) and (02:50)   23 ✓

14 (05:50) and (06:10)   20 ✓

15 (07:51) and (08:00)   9 ✓

16 (12:01) and (12:40)   39 ✓

17 (04:52) and (05:10)   18 ✓   6

Underline the correct answer on each line.

18 100 − 29 =   81   79   71   89   129 ✓

19 56 ÷ 7 =   8   9   7   6   10   47 ✓

20 47 + 35 =   72   73   81   71   82 ✓ +35 / 8 2 / 47

21 $\frac{1}{2} + \frac{1}{2}$ = $\frac{1}{4}$ $\frac{1}{2}$ 1 ✓   2   4   4 4

22–23 Fill in the missing numbers on this number line.

−2   −1   0   1   2   3   4 ✓

24–25 Fill in the missing numbers on this number line.

−5   −4   −3   −2   −1   0   1 ✓

26–29 Fill in the missing numbers on this number line.

−7   −6   −5   −4   −3   −2   −1 ✓   8 8

Maria was born 5 July 2004.   Anita was born 19 April 2004.

Daley was born 31 October 2004.   David was born 8 June 2003.

30–31 Maria ✗ is the eldest and Daley ✓ is the youngest.

3

32–34 On 5 July 2006 Maria was __1 X__ , Anita was __1 X__
and __David__ was 3. ✓

35–37   × 6

12	18	X
20	26	X
40	46	X

38–40   + 5

60	65	✓
80	85	✓
90	95	✓

Now go to the Progress Chart to record your score!   Total ③4 / 40

Paper 2

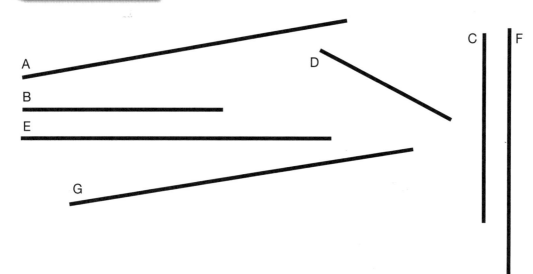

Measure each line and answer the questions.

1 The longest sloping line is __G__ ✓.

2 The longest vertical line is __F__ ✓.

3 The longest horizontal line is __Ð (E)__ ✓.

4 What is the difference in length between the two horizontal lines?
__3__ ✓ cm

5 What is the difference in length between the two vertical lines?
__1½__ ✓ cm

6 The two vertical lines added together are __11½__ ✓ cm long.

7 The two horizontal lines added together are __14__ ✓ cm long.

4

8 What is the **product** of 5 and 7?   35 ✓   ①1

There are 60 children altogether in Class 2 and Class 3.

   9 If there are 32 in Class 2, how many are in Class 3?   28 ✓

George has three times as much money as Michael.

   10 Michael has 14p, so how much has George?   42p ✓   ②2

$$\begin{array}{r} 1\!4 \\ \times\, 3 \\ \hline 4\,2 \end{array}$$

   312   123   321

   11 In which number is the figure 1 a unit?   321 ✓

   12 In which number is the figure 1 a ten?   312 ✓

   13 In which number is the figure 1 a hundred?   123 ✓   ③3

   14 What number needs to go in the box? Write it in.

     4732 = | 4000 | + 700 + 30 + 2   ✓

   15 What number needs to go in the box? Write it in.

     5935 = 5000 + | 900 | + 30 + 5   ✓

   16 What number needs to go in the box? Write it in.

     3941 = 3000 + 900 + | 40 | + 1   ✓

   17 What number needs to go in the box? Write it in.

     5864 = 5000 + 800 + 60 + | 4 | ✓

   18 What number needs to go in the box? Write it in.

     9573 = | 9000 | + 500 + 70 + 3   ✓

   19 What number needs to go in the box? Write it in.

     1633 = 1000 + | 600 | + 30 + 3   ✓

   20 What number needs to go in the box? Write it in.

     7488 = 7000 + 400 + | 80 | + 8   ✓   ⑦7

21–22 Fill in the missing numbers on this number line.

13   15   17   19   _21_   23   25   _27_   ② 2

Underline the correct answer in each line.

23 £1 – 11p   =   1p   (89p)   £1.11   99p   £1.01 ✓

24 8p + 6p + 7p =   20p   22p   19p   (21p)   23p ✓

25 66 + 26   =   (92)   87   82   83   93 ✓

26 105 ÷ 3   =   15   33   (35)   41   51 ✓

27 ½ of 40   =   80   10   2   40   (20) ✓

28 1000 ÷ 10   =   500   10   20   (100)   1000 ✓   ⑥ 6

Mum, Dad, Helen and Andrew went to the zoo.

Chartwell Zoo

Entrance: Adults   £22.50
Children   £15.50
Monkey House: £5.00
Ice Cream: £1.60

29 How much did it cost for all of them to go in? £85.0p ✗

30 How much did it cost for all of them to go in the monkey house?
£105 ✗

31 How much did it cost for all of them to have an ice cream? £94.40

32 How much did they spend at the zoo altogether? £85   £28.40 ✗ ○ 4

There were 35 children in a class.

33–34 If the number of boys was one more than the number of girls, there
are _18_ boys and _17_ girls.   ② 2

6

Here is part of a ruler.

35 How far is it from A to G? _6cm_ ✓

36 How far is it from B to E? _2½cm_ ✓

37 How far is it from D to H? _5½cm_ ✓

38 How far is it from C to F? _3½cm_ ✓ ④ 4

39 What number, when divided by 9 gives an answer of 6? _54_ ✓

40 How many times will 10 go into 200? _20 times_ ✓ ② 2

Now go to the Progress Chart to record your score! Total ㊱ 40

Paper 3

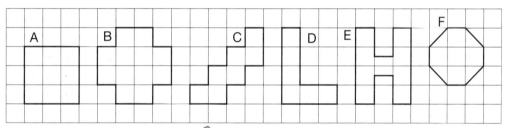

1 The area of shape A is _9_ squares. ✓

2 The area of shape B is _12_ squares. ✓

3 The area of shape C is _7_ squares. ✓

4 The area of shape D is _6_ squares. ✓

5 The area of shape E is _9_ squares. ✓

6 The area of shape F is _7_ squares. ✓ ⑥ 6

7 In every 2 weeks I spend 10 days at school. So in every 5 weeks I spend _25_ days at school. ✓

8 In every 3 days I spend 4 hours reading. So in every __5__ days ✗
I spend 20 hours reading.   15

9 With every box of cereal you get 4 tokens, and the toy you want
requires 24 tokens.
How many boxes of cereal do you have to buy?   _6_ ✓

10 In every *Kid's App* magazine you get 3 transfers. In 3 *Kid's App*
magazines you get __9__ transfers. ✓   3 | 4

11–15 Underline the numbers which can be divided exactly by 5.

52   25 ✓   40 ✓   24   45 ✓   54   60 ✓   51   15 ✓   5 | 5

16 Write in words 7001. _Seven-thousand and one_ ✓   1 | 1

Church

Bus
station

School

Railway
station

```
      N
NW    ↑   NE
W ←——╳——→ E
SW    ↓   SE
      S
```

Castle

In which direction is:

17 the school from the railway station?   East ✗ W

18 the castle from the school?   South ✓

19 the bus station from the school?   NW ✓

20 the church from the bus station?   NE ✓

21 the railway station from church?   NW ✗ SE

22 the castle from the church?   South ✓

23 the school from the bus station?   NW ✗ SE   7

What number is halfway between:

24 50 and 70? _60_ ✓

25 35 and 55? _45_ ✓

26 25 and 35? _30_ ✓

27 12 and 20? _16_ ✓ ④ 4

28 Jane was born in 2008. Jock is 3 years older than Jane. In what year was he born? _2005_ ✓

29 Leanne was born in 2005. In what year was she 6? _2011_ ✓

30 Rehman was 12 in 2011. In what year was she born? _1999_ ✓ ③ 3

31–33 Reflect these shapes in the **mirror line**.

③ 3

34 What is the biggest number you can make with these **digits**: 3, 6, 4, 8? _8643_ ✓

35 Now write it in words. _eight thousand, six hundred and forty-three_ ✓

36 What is the biggest number you can make with these **digits**: 2, 3, 4, 0? _4320_ ✓

37 Now write it in words. _four thousand, three hundred and twenty._ ✓

38 Write in figures three thousand, two hundred and fifty-four. _3254_ ✓ ⑤ 5

39 What is one quarter of 60? _15_ ✓

40 How many minutes are there between 10:45 and 11:10? _30 min_ ✓ ① 2

Now go to the Progress Chart to record your score! Total ㉟ 40

9

Paper 4

1   73
     35
 + 98
  206 ✓

2   58
  × 6
  348 ✓

3   £6.98
 + £0.42
  £7.40 ✓

③ **3**

4–9 Fill in the missing numbers to balance the scales.

21 + 3	24	6 × 4	✓
5 × 7	35	28 + 7	✓
70 − 10	60	5 × 12	✓
45 − 3	42	6 × 7	✓
6 × 9	54	60 − 6	✓
17 + 23	40	50 − 10	✓

$$\begin{array}{r} 3\,4\,0 \\ -\ 1\,7 \\ \hline 2\,3 \end{array}$$

⑥ **6**

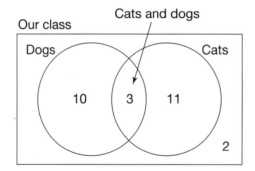

Our class made this **Venn diagram** to show how many of us have cats and dogs.

10 How many children have dogs?   13 ✓

11 How many have cats?   14 ✓

12 How many have both a cat and a dog?   3 ✓

13 How many children haven't got a dog?   13 ✓

14 How many children haven't got a cat?   12 ✓

15 How many children are there in the class?   26 ✓

⑥ **6**

16 When a number was added to 16 the answer was 25. What was the number?

$$\begin{array}{r} 25 \\ -16 \\ \hline 09 \end{array}$$

_9_ ✓ ① 1

17 What temperature does this thermometer show?

-1 °C

| -5 | -4 | -3 | -2 | -1 | 0 | 1 | 2 | 3 | 4 |

°C

18 Draw a circle around the lowest temperature: -7 °C,   (-9 °C) ✓   ② 2

19 Kay was 9 in 2010. In what year was she born?   2001 ✓

20 Martin was born in December 2007 and Michael was born in January 2008.

Who is the elder?   Martin ✓   ② 2

This **pictogram** shows the number of children in our school.

Farm Lane	웃	웃	웃									
High Street	웃	웃	웃	웃	웃	웃	웃	웃	웃	웃		
Birch Avenue	웃	웃	웃	웃	웃	웃	웃	웃	웃			
Riverside Road	웃	웃	웃	웃	웃	웃	웃	웃	웃	웃	웃	웃
Manor Road	웃	웃	웃	웃	웃							

Key

웃 = 10 children

웃 = 5 children

21 How many children are there in the school?   360 ✓

22 In which road or street do most children live?   Riverside Road ✓

23 Twice as many children live in the High Street as in   Manor Road ✓

24 There are three times as many children in Birch Avenue as in   Farm Lane ✓

25–28 Twenty more children come to our school. Five live in Farm Lane, 5 in Riverside Road and 10 in Birch Avenue. Show this on the **pictogram**. ✓

29 How many will there now be in our school?   370 ✗   ⑧ 9

11

30 How much greater is 33 than 19?   14 ✓

31 I spent 77p and had 15p left. How much did I have at first?   92p ✓

32 What is the cost of 3 packets of crisps at 26p each?   78p ✓   ③ 3

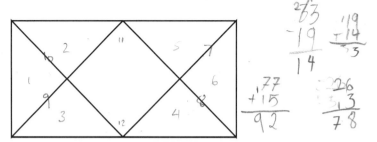

$$\overset{2}{\cancel{3}}\overset{1}{3}$$
-19
14

$^{1}19$
$+14$
$\overline{~~3}$

$_{1}77$
$+15$
$\overline{92}$

$^{2}26$
$\times 3$
$\overline{78}$

Look closely at the shape above.

33 How many **squares** does it contain?   1

34 How many rectangles does it contain?   1 × 2

35 How many triangles does it contain?   10 × 12   ① 3

One question on each line has a different answer from the others.

Draw a line under it.

36   5 × 10   45 + 5 ⁵⁰   10 × 5 ⁵⁰   <u>60 − 5</u> ⁵⁵   47 + 3 ⁵⁰ ✓

37   <u>7 × 6</u> ⁴²   4 × 12 ⁴⁸   6 × 8 ⁴⁸   42 + 6 ⁴⁸   50 − 2 ⁴⁸ ✓   ② 2

38 What number is 1 less than 300?   299 ✓

39 The number which is 2 more than 278 is   290 × 280

40 If I took 10 from 106 it would leave   96 ✓   ② 3

Now go to the Progress Chart to record your score!   Total �37 40

Paper 5

HIGHER !

1 Draw a circle around the highest temperature: −8 °C,   −9 °C ✓

2–3 Fill in the missing numbers on this number line.

<u>−2</u>   −1   0   1   2   <u>3</u>   4 ✓   ③ 3

12

Underline the correct answer in each line.

4 11 × 11   =   110   111   <u>121</u>   132   122 ✓

5 150 ÷ 30   =   50   <u>5</u>   30   20   55 ✓

6 70 − 39   =   41   49   39   109   <u>31</u> ✓

7 $1\frac{1}{2}$ hours   =   <u>75 min</u>   90 min   45 min   85 min   15 min ✗   90 min

8 1.5 kg   =   150 g   505 g   1500 g   1050 g   105 g ✓

9 510 ÷ 5   =   21   102   120   <u>12</u>   121 ✗ 102

10 150 cm   =   15 m   0.15 m   150 m   50 m   1.5 m ✓

12
5$\overline{)510}$ 6 7̶0̶
              − 3 9
              3 1

⑤ ⑦

A   3 cm

7 cm

11 What is the **area** of rectangle A? ___21___ cm² ✓

12 What is the **perimeter** of rectangle A? ___20___ cm ✓

B   3 cm

17 cm

13 What is the **area** of rectangle B? ___40___ cm² ✗ 51

14 What is the **perimeter** of rectangle B? ___40___ cm ✓

1 7
× 3
4 0

③ ④

Fill in the missing number in each question.

15 3 + 4 + ___3___ = 10 ✓

16 5 + 1 − ___2___ = 4 ✓

17 3 + 3 + ___3___ = 9 ✓

③ ③

18–22 Underline the numbers which are **divisible** by 7.

    19   <u>49</u>   <u>28</u>   <u>56</u>   62   <u>35</u>   <u>77</u>   79   5 | 5

23–26 Underline the numbers which are **multiples** of 6.

    <u>36</u>   <u>72</u>   26   <u>96</u>   56   <u>24</u>   28   4 | 4

Here is part of a centimetre ruler.

    cm

27 How far is it from A to B?   2 cm ✓

28 How far is it from C to D? $\frac{1}{2}$ cm ✓

29 How far is it from A to D?   3 $\frac{1}{2}$ cm ✓

30 How far is it from B to F?   4 cm ✓

31 How far is it from C to G?   4 cm ✓

32 How far is it from E to G?   2 $\frac{1}{2}$ cm ✓   6 | 6

Write the next two numbers in each line.

33–34   6   12   18   24   30   <u>36</u> <u>42</u> ✓✓

35–36   50   47   44   41   38   <u>35</u> <u>32</u> ✓✓   4 | 4

Underline the larger of each pair.

37 (6×10) or (3×22) ✓

38 (5×20) or (11×10) ✓

39 $(\underline{10 \times 10})$ or (3×30) ✓

40 (3×50) or $(\underline{4 \times 40})$ ✓   4 | 4

Paper 6

1
$$37 + 46 = 83$$ ✓

2
$$^672 - 39 = 33$$ ✓

3
$$36 \times 3 = 108$$ ✓

4
$$\frac{54}{2) \overline{108}}$$ ✓

4 | 4

5–10 Complete the following bus timetable. Each bus takes the same amount of time to do the journey.

Bus	A	B	C	
High Street	2:40	3:50	5:00 ✗	4:55
Broad Lane	2:50 2:45 ✗	4:00	5:05	
Market Place	2:55	4:05 ✓	5:10 ✓	
Kent Road	3:05	4:15 4:10 ✗	4:20 5:15 ✗	

2 | 6

Two shelves are 65 cm and 89 cm long.

11 What is their total length in metres?

1 m 54 cm ✓

12 What is the difference in their lengths in centimetres?

24 cm ✓

2 | 2

$$\begin{array}{r}89 \\ -65 \\ \hline 24\end{array}$$

$$\begin{array}{r}89 \\ +65 \\ \hline 154\end{array}$$

13 What fraction of the circle is spotted?

½ ✓

14 What fraction is striped?

¼ ✓

15 What fraction is plain?

¼ ✓

16 How many times larger is the spotted part than the striped part?

2 times ✓ larger

4 | 4

17–23 Complete the empty brackets in this multiplication table.

×	4	5	(20)
	(5)	10	(50)
	12	( )	18
	( )	20	( )
	20	( )	

24 164 × 4 = 656 ✓

$$\begin{array}{r} 164 \\ \times\ 4 \\ \hline 656 \end{array}$$

25 182 × 6 = 1092 ✓

$$\begin{array}{r} 182 \\ *\ \ 6 \\ \hline 1092 \end{array}$$

Put the correct sign in the spaces.

26–27   3 _+_ 4 = 6 _+_ 1 ✓

28–29   5 _+_ 4 = 2 _+_ 7 ✓

30–31   3 _+_ × 3 = 8 _+_ 1 ✓

32–33   8 _−_ 1 = 5 _+_ 2 ✓

This **pictogram** shows how the children in Class 4 come to school.

Key

♀ = 1 child

34 How many children are there in the class?   25 ✓

35 How many more walk than come by car?   6 ✓

36 How many more come by car than by bus?   1 ✓

37 How many children don't come by bus?   20 ✓

38 How many more children walk than come by bus?   7 ✓

39 How many children don't come by train?   23 ✓

40 How many times can I take 9 from 54?   6 times ✓

Now go to the Progress Chart to record your score!   Total 32 40

16

Paper 7

1 $345 \div 5 = $ _69_ ✓

2 $345 + 456 = $ _801_ ✓

3 $321 \times 3 = $ _963_ ✓

(7) 3

4–6 Fill in the missing numbers on this number line.

| -7 | _−6_ ✓ | -5 | _−4_ ✓ | -3 | _−2_ ✓ | -1 |

(3) 3

7 Draw a circle around the highest temperature: (−17 °C), -29 °C ✓

8–12 Put these temperature in order, lowest first.

0 °C, -4 °C, -7 °C,   3 °C, -1 °C   _−7°C, −4°C, −3°C, −1°C, 0°C_ ✓ (4) 6

13 My watch was 5 minutes fast. It showed 10:30.
What was the right time?   _10_ : _25_ ✓   (1) 1

Afternoon school begins at 1:30 and finishes at 3:35.

14 For how long do we work in the afternoon?   _2_ hr _5_ min ✓

15 What change should I have from £1.00 if I spent 67p?   _33_ p ✓ (2) 2

16–20 Change this recipe for ginger nuts for 6 people to a recipe for 12
people for a party.

6 people	
125 g	flour
30 g	fat
75 g	sugar
30 ml	treacle
1 teaspoon	ground ginger

12 people	
_250_ g ✓	flour
_60_ g ✓	fat
_150_ g ✓	sugar
_60_ ml ✓	treacle
_2_ teaspoons	ground ginger

125
250

75
+75
150

(5) 5

Underline the question in each line which does not have the same answer as
the others.

21   4×3 12 6×2 12 12×1 12 4×2 ✓

22	4×4	8×2	1×16	$\underline{3 \times 5}$ ✓
23	6×5	$\underline{9 \times 4}$	10×3	15×2 ✓
24	$20 \div 4$	$\underline{25 \div 6}$	$10 \div 2$	$15 \div 3$ ✓
25	$16 - 7$	$18 \div 2$	3×3	$\underline{4 + 6}$ ✓
26	$\underline{36 \div 3}$	6×3	$25 - 7$	$7 + 11$ ✓

6 6

Farway
450 km
Tagos
250 km
Boxo
300 km
270 km
100 km
Berrytown
Dingo
Manley

27 Which town is the furthest away from Boxo?

Farway ✓

28 Which town is the nearest to Boxo?

Berrytown ✓

29 How much further is it from Boxo to Farway than it is from Boxo to Manley?

180 km ✓ 3 3

$$
\begin{array}{r}
450 \\
-270 \\
\hline 180
\end{array}
$$

30–31 Underline the smallest number and circle the largest.

    5.7   4.8   7.5   (8.4)   <u>4.5</u>

2 2

32 Convert metres into centimetres: 7.45 m = <u>745</u> cm ✓

33 **Round** to the nearest pound: £7.49 = £ 7 ✓

34 Convert centimetres into metres: 824 cm = <u>8.24</u> m ✓

35 Write 345p in £.   345p = £<u>3.45p</u> ✓

4 4

    A   B   C   D   E

36–37 Shade in the **quadrilaterals** above.

A   B   C   D   E

38–40 Shade in the **pentagons** above.

⑤ 5

Now go to the Progress Chart to record your score!   Total ㉘ 40

Paper 8

1 How many pence in £1.25?

2 How many pence in £0.29?

125p ✓
_____
29p

② 2

A _____

B _____

C _____

D _____

E _____

F _____

3 Line A is 6.5 cm long. ✓

4 Line B is 8 cm long. ✓ ⎱ 14.5cm

5 Line C is 3 cm long. ✓

6 Line D is 7.5 cm long. ✓

7 Line E is 7 cm long. ✓ 14.5cm

8 Line F is 8.5 cm long. ✓

9 What is the difference in length between the longest and the shortest line?

5.5 cm ✓

10–11 Lines A and B put together would be the same length as lines E ✓ and D put together. ✓

E ✓

⑨ 9

A   B   C

12–14 A has _250_ ml.   B has _400_ ml.   C has _150_ ml. ✓

How many ml of water would you have to add to each jug so that each one holds half a litre?

15–17 A needs _350_ ml.   B needs _100_ ml. ✓   C needs _450_ ml.   (4) 6

18 What is the remainder when 40 is divided by 6?   _____   (0) 1

In the number 1234:   how many tens are there?   3

                  how many hundreds are there?   2

19 In the number 135:   how many tens are there?   _3_ ✓

20   how many hundreds are there?   _1_ ✓

21 In the number 1247:   how many units are there?   _7_ ✓

22   how many hundreds are there?   _2_ ✓

23 In the number 2439:   how many tens are there?   _3_ ✓

24   how many thousands are there?   _2_ ✓   (6) 6

25 What is $\frac{1}{2}$ of 22?   _11_ ✓

26 $\frac{1}{3}$ of 24 is   _6_ 8

27 $\frac{1}{4}$ of 20 is   _5_ ✓

28 What is $\frac{1}{5}$ of 15?   _3_ ✓

29 $\frac{1}{10}$ of 40 is   _4_ ✓

30 $\frac{1}{3}$ of 27 is   _9_ ✓   (5) 6

What are the names of these shapes?

Use the following words to help you:

sphere   triangular prism   **cuboid**   **cube**   cylinder

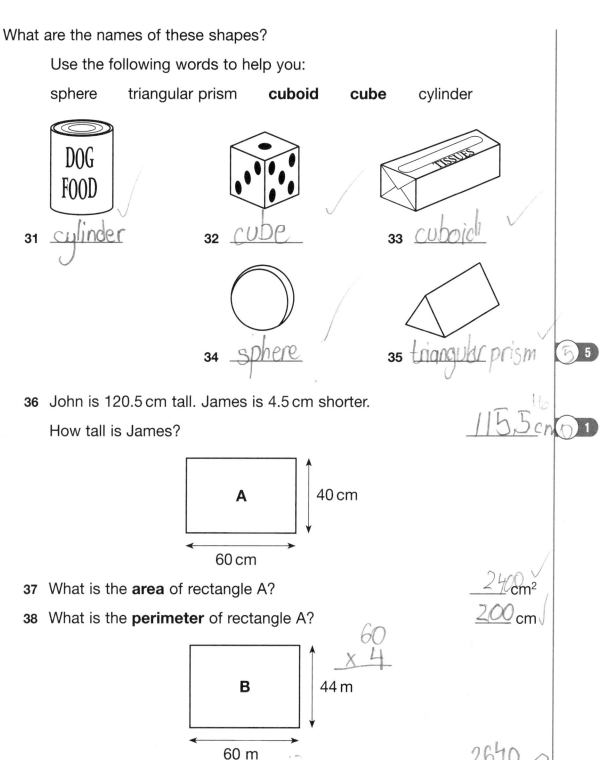

31 _cylinder_ ✓

32 _cube_ ✓

33 _cuboid_ ✓

34 _sphere_ ✓

35 _triangular prism_ ✓   ⑤ 5

36 John is 120.5 cm tall. James is 4.5 cm shorter.

How tall is James?

_115.5 cm_ ⓪ 1   ¹¹⁶

37 What is the **area** of rectangle A?   _240 cm²_ ✓

38 What is the **perimeter** of rectangle A?   _200 cm_ ✓

(rectangle A: 40 cm height, 60 cm width)

(rectangle B: 44 m height, 60 m width)

60
× 4

39 What is the **area** of rectangle B?   2640   _244 m²_ ✗

40 What is the **perimeter** of rectangle B?   _208 m_ ✓   ④ 4

Now go to the Progress Chart to record your score!   Total ㊱ 40

21

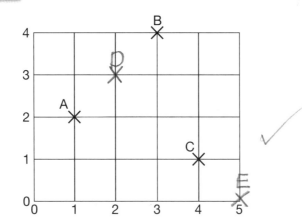

A is 1 square along and 2 squares up from (0,0).

1–2 B is __3__ squares along and __4__ squares up from (0,0). ✓

3–4 C is __4__ squares along and __1__ square up from (0,0). ✓

A is at the point (1,2).

5 B is at the point (__3__, __4__). ✓

6 C is at the point (__4__, __1__). ✓

7 D is at the point (2,3). Mark it on the grid above.

8 E is at the point (5,0). Mark it on the grid above.

⑧ 8

9
```
   4.9
 + 7.5
──────
  12.4
  1
```
✓

10
```
   3.9
 ×   8
──────
  31.2
  7
```
✓

② 2

11 Share 20 cherries among 5 children. They have __4__ each. ✓

12 How many glasses holding $\frac{1}{2}$ litre could be filled from a jug which holds $7\frac{1}{2}$ litres?   15 ✓

13 Sally missed the 9:25 a.m. bus. The next one is 17 minutes later. At what time is the next bus?   9:42 ✓

14 I had 9p after spending 24p. How much did I have at first?   33p ✓

15 Aziz walks 4 km each day. In November he walks __120__ km. ✓

⑤ 5

Here is a bar chart which shows the number of hours of sunshine we had each day in the last week of June.

Mon Tues Wed Thurs Fri Sat Sun
9   1   8   6   3   10   5

16–17 Which 2 days added together had the same amount of sunshine as Saturday?

Monday and _Tuesday_ ✓

18 It rained on only one day in the week. On which day did it probably rain?

Tuesday ✓

19–21 On which 3 days together did the total sunshine equal that of Monday?

Sunday ✓, _Friday_ ✓ and _Tuesday_ ✓

22 How many days had fewer than 6 hours of sunshine? ___3___ ✓

23 How many days had more than 8 hours of sunshine? ___2___ ✓

24 What was the total hours of sunshine for the week? ___42___ ✓

25–30 The sunniest day was Saturday. Write the other days in the order of sunniest day to least sunny day.

Saturday, ___Mon___ ✓, ___Wed___ ✓, ___Thurs___ ✓,

___Sun___ ✓, ___Fri___ ✓, ___Tues___ ✓.

15/15

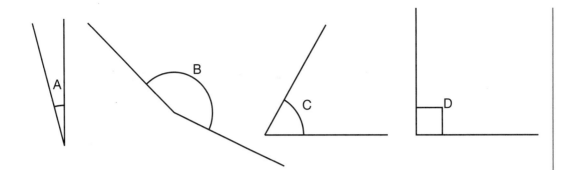

Look at the above angles and answer the following questions.

31 Which angle is the right angle? _D_ ✓

32 The smallest angle is _A_ ✓ .

33 The largest angle is _B_ ✓ .

34 _C_ ✓ is the 60° angle.

35–38 Place the angles in order of size from smallest to largest.

_A_ ✓ is less than _C_ ✓ is less than _D_ ✓ is less than _B_ ✓ .   ⑧ 8

39 Using the **digits** 5, 6 and 7 make as many 3-figure numbers as you
can.

567 ✓ 576 ✓ 675 ✓ 657 ✓ 756 ✓ 763 ✓
×   ×
                                              198 ✓   ② 2

40 Now take away the smallest from the largest. _198_

Now go to the Progress Chart to record your score!   Total 40 40

Paper 10

1 Write the correct number in the box.

231 →(75 less is)→ [156]

```
  2 1
 '2̶3̶'1̶   ✓
-  75
 1 5 6
```

2 Write the correct number in the box.

[322] →(62 less is)→ 260   ✓   ② 2

3 Put these numbers in order, smallest to largest.

7536	~~6537~~	~~5736~~	6573
5736 ✓	6537 ✓	6573 ✓	7538 ✓

1 ✓

Look at this grid.

4 How many **squares** of this size are in the grid?

1 ✓

5 How many **squares** of this size are in the grid?

4 ✓

6 How many **squares** of this size are in the grid?

9 ✓

7 What is the total number of **squares** in the grid?

14 ✓

4 4

8 What is the smallest number you can make with these **digits**: 3, 5, 4, 9?

3459 ✓

9 Now write it in words.

Three Thousand Four Hundred and Fifty-nine. ✓

10 What is the largest number you can make with these **digits**: 3, 5, 4, 9?

9543 ✓

11 Now write it in words.

Nine Thousand Five Hundred and Forty-Three. ✓

12 What is the smallest number you can make with these **digits**: 9, 5, 8, 6, 1?

15689 ✓

13 Now write it in words.

Fifteen Thousand Six Hundred and Eighty-nine. ✓

14 What is the largest number you can make with these **digits:** 9, 5, 8, 6, 1?   98,651 ✓

15 Now write it in words.
  Ninety-Eight Thousand Six Hundred and Fifty-One ✓

16 Write in figures one thousand, four hundred and eighty-nine. 1489 ✓

17 Write in figures seven thousand and eighty-nine.   7089 ✓   10

Here is a **pictogram** which shows what kind of books are liked most by children in Readwell School.

Key ☺ = 10 children

Mysteries	☺	☺	☺	☺	☺	☺	☺	☺		80 –
Travel	☺	☺	☺	☺						40 –
School Stories	☺	☺	☺	☺	☺	☺	☺	☺	☺	90 –
Books on Hobbies	☺	☺	☺							30 –
Animal Stories	☺	☺	☺	☺	☺	☺	☺			70 –

18 Which type of book is most popular?   School Stories ✓

19 Which type of book is least popular?   Books on Hobbies ✓

20 How many children are in the school?   310 ✓

21 Which kind of book is twice as popular as travel books?   Mysteries ✓

22 How many more children like mysteries than animal stories?   10 ✓

23 How many more children prefer school stories to travel books?   50 ✓   6

Underline the right answer in each line.

24 **Round** £3.70 to the nearest pound: £3   __£4__   £7   £10   £70

25 **Round** £26.01 to the nearest pound: £20   £25   __£26__   £27   £30   2

26
$$\begin{array}{r} £ \\ {}^{3}4.39 \\ -\ 1.72 \\ \hline £2.67 \end{array}$$ ✓

27
$$\begin{array}{r} £ \\ 0.27 \\ \times\ {}_{3}5 \\ \hline £1.35 \end{array}$$ ✓   2

26

Ring the correct answer.

28 When you add together two odd numbers the answer is:

an odd number   (an even number) ✓

29 If you add together two even numbers the answer is:

an odd number   (an even number) ✓

30 If you add together three even numbers the answer is:

an odd number   (an even number) ✓

31 If you add together three odd numbers the answer is:

(an odd number)   an even number ✓

④ 4

32 What is the **sum** of the even numbers between 3 and 7?   10 ✓

33 What is the difference between 7 and 19?   12 ✓   ② 2

34 How many times can I take £1.25 from £6.25?   5 ✓   ① 1

Write the correct fraction in each space.

$£6.25$ 1
$-£1.25$

£5.00

$-£1.25$ 2

£3.75

$-£1.25$ 3

£2.50

$-£1.23$

£1.25 +

5

35 Shaded   1/4 ✓

36 Unshaded   3/4 ✓

37 Shaded   1/5 ✓

38 Unshaded   4/5 ✓

39 Shaded   2/3 ✓

40 Unshaded   1/3 ✓

⑥ 6

Paper 11

1 Sally left home at 08:52 and arrived at school at 09:01.

How long did it take her to walk to school? _9 min_ ✓

2 If I spent 23p and had 18p left, how much had I at first? _41_ p ✓

3 How many children are there altogether in a school if
there are 197 boys and 165 girls? _362_ ③ 3

197
+ 165

197   23
       + 8

Here are four regular pizzas. One whole, one cut in halves, one in thirds and one in sixths.

4 How many $\frac{1}{6}$s make 1 whole? _6_ ✓

5 How many $\frac{1}{6}$s make $\frac{1}{3}$? _2_ ✓

6 How many $\frac{1}{6}$s make $\frac{1}{2}$? _3_ ✓

7 How many $\frac{1}{3}$s make 1 whole? _3_ ✓

8 How many $\frac{1}{6}$s make $\frac{2}{3}$? _4_ ✓ ⑤ 5

9
```
   369
   425
 + 264
```
_1048_ ✗   X 1058

10
```
   204
 ×   8
```
_1632_ ✓
   3
① 2

11 How many times can I take 9 from 99? _11_ ✓

12 From the **digits** 4, 5 and 6 make a number so that the
5 is the hundred and the 4 is the unit. _564_ ✓

13 Write in figures two thousand and twenty. _2020_ ✓

28

14 How many times can I take 8 from 56? <u>7</u> ✓

4 **4**

15–17 Shade in the **hexagons**.

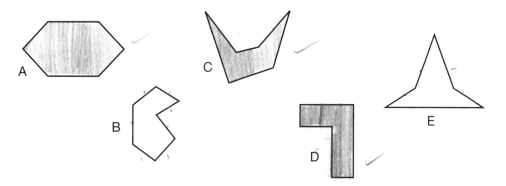

A ✓ C ✓ B D ✓ E

3 **3**

18–24 Here are the ingredients for a meal for 1 person.

Jacket Potato with Leeks and Cheese for 1 person	
1 large (about 200 g)	potato
10 g	butter
1 tablespoon	milk
2 (about 150 g)	leeks
40 g	grated cheese

£3.75
.75
£23.980
.75
£2.25
75
£9.48 10
75
.75 p
3.75

Increase the measurements to change it to a recipe for 4 people.

Jacket Potato with Leeks and Cheese for 4 people	
✓ <u>4</u> large (about <u>800</u> g)	potatoes
✓ <u>40</u> g	butter
✓ <u>4</u> tablespoons	milk
✓ <u>8</u> (about <u>600</u> g)	leeks
✗ <u>100</u> g	grated cheese

160

6 **7**

25–26 18 is half of ✗ <u>9</u>, and three times as much as <u>6</u> ✓.

27 How many jars of Bovo, each costing 75p, can I buy with £3.75? 4 ✗

1 **3**

s

This clock shows the correct time.

How fast or slow are the clocks below?

Write the number of minutes and ring the correct word for each clock.

28–29 __5__ minutes   (fast) ✓
                           slow
                ✓

30–31 __10__ minutes   fast
                ✓   (slow) ✓

32–33 __20__ minutes   fast
                ✓   (slow) ✓

6 | 6

34–38 Each train takes 1 hr 10 min to reach Fordby. Write what time each one arrives.

	Train A	Train B	Train C	Train D	Train E
Leaves Bunmouth at	10:00	11:30	12:50	13:55	15:10
Arrives at Fordby at	11:10 ✓	12:40 ✓	13:00 ✗	15:05 ✓	16:20 ✓

14:00

4 | 5

Put a sign in each space so that each question will be correct.

39   5 __−__ 2 = 2 __+__ 1 ✓

40   4 __+__ 4 = 10 __−__ 2 ✓

2 | 2

Paper 1

1. 5
2. 3
3. 4
4. 5
5. 6
6. 8
7. 14
8. 6
9. a square
10. 6
11. a rectangle
12. 11 min
13. 23 min
14. 20 min
15. 9 min
16. 39 min
17. 18 min
18. 71
19. 8
20. 82
21. 1
22. 0
23. 2
24. −3
25. −1
26. −7
27. −5
28. −3
29. −1
30. David
31. Daley
32. 2
33. 2
34. David
35. 72
36. 120
37. 240
38. 65
39. 85
40. 95

Paper 2

1. G
2. F
3. E
4. 3
5. 1.5
6. 11.5
7. 14
8. 35
9. 28
10. 42p
11. 321
12. 312
13. 123
14. 4000
15. 900
16. 40
17. 4
18. 9000
19. 600
20. 80
21. 21
22. 27
23. 89p
24. 21p
25. 92
26. 35
27. 20
28. 100
29. £76.00
30. £20.00
31. £6.40
32. £102.40
33. 18
34. 17
35. 6 cm
36. 2.5 cm or 25 mm
37. 5.5 cm or 55 mm
38. 3.5 cm or 35 mm
39. 54
40. 20

Paper 3

1. 9
2. 12
3. 7
4. 6
5. 9
6. 7
7. 25
8. 15
9. 6
10. 9
11. 25
12. 40
13. 45
14. 60
15. 15
16. seven thousand and one
17. W
18. S
19. NW
20. NE
21. SE
22. S
23. SE
24. 60
25. 45
26. 30
27. 16
28. 2005
29. 2011
30. 1999

31–33

34. 8643
35. eight thousand, six hundred and forty-three
36. 4320
37. four thousand three hundred and twenty
38. 3254
39. 15
40. 25

Bond Maths Assessment Papers 8–9 years

ANSWERS

Paper 4

1 206
2 348
3 £7.40
4 4
5 7
6 12
7 3
8 6
9 23
10 13
11 14
12 3
13 13
14 12
15 26
16 9
17 −1 °C
18 −9 °C
19 2001
20 Martin
21 360
22 Riverside Road
23 Manor Road
24 Farm Lane

25–28

| Farm Lane | | | |
| Riverside Road | | | |

29 380
30 14
31 92
32 78
33 1
34 2 (Remember, a square is a rectangle with 4 equal sides.)
35 12
36 60 − 5
37 7 × 6
38 299
39 280
40 96

Paper 5

1 −8 °C
2 −2
3 3
4 121
5 5
6 31
7 90 min
8 1500 g
9 102
10 1.5 m
11 21
12 20
13 51
14 40
15 3
16 2
17 3
18 49
19 28
20 56
21 35
22 77
23 36
24 72
25 96
26 24
27 2 cm
28 0.5 cm or 5 mm
29 3.5 cm or 35 mm
30 4 cm
31 4 cm
32 2.5 cm or 25 mm
33 36
34 42
35 35
36 32
37 3 × 22
38 11 × 10
39 10 × 10
40 4 × 40

Paper 6

1 83
2 33
3 108
4 54

5–10

Bus	A	B	C
High Street	2:40	3:50	**4:55**
Broad Lane	**2:50**	4:00	5:05
Market Place	2:55	**4:05**	**5:10**
Kent Road	3:05	**4:15**	**5:20**

11 1.54 m or 154 cm
12 24 cm
13 $\frac{1}{2}$ or $\frac{2}{4}$
14 $\frac{1}{4}$
15 $\frac{1}{4}$
16 twice

17–23

×	4	5	(6)
2	(8)	10	(12)
3	12	(15)	18
4	(16)	20	(24)
5	20	(25)	30

24 656
25 1092
26 +
27 +
28 +
29 +
30 ×
31 +
32 −
33 +
34 25
35 6
36 1
37 20
38 7
39 23
40 6

Bond Maths Assessment Papers 8–9 years

A2

Paper 7

1. 69
2. 801
3. 963
4. −6
5. −4
6. −2
7. −17 °C
8. −7 °C
9. −4 °C
10. −1 °C
11. 0 °C
12. 3 °C
13. 10:25
14. 2 hr 5 min
15. 33
16. 250
17. 60
18. 150
19. 60
20. 2
21. 4 × 2
22. 3 × 5
23. 9 × 4
24. 25 ÷ 6
25. 4 + 6
26. 36 ÷ 3
27. Farway
28. Berrytown
29. 180 km
30. 4.5
31. 8.4
32. 745 cm
33. £7
34. 8.24 m
35. £3.45
36. B
37. E
38. B
39. D
40. E

Paper 8

1. 125
2. 29
3. 6.5
4. 8
5. 3
6. 7.5
7. 7
8. 8.5
9. 5.5
10. D
11. E
12. 250
13. 400
14. 150
15. 250
16. 100
17. 350
18. 4
19. 3
20. 1
21. 7
22. 2
23. 3
24. 2
25. 11
26. 8
27. 5
28. 3
29. 4
30. 9
31. cylinder
32. cube
33. cuboid
34. sphere
35. triangular prism
36. 116 cm
37. 2400
38. 200
39. 2640
40. 208

Paper 9

1. 3
2. 4
3. 4
4. 1
5. (3,4)
6. (4,1)

7–8

9. 12.4
10. 31.2
11. 4
12. 15
13. 9:42 a.m.
14. 33p
15. 120 km
16. Monday
17. Tuesday
18. Tuesday
19. Tuesday
20. Friday
21. Sunday
22. 3
23. 2
24. 42
25. Monday
26. Wednesday
27. Thursday
28. Sunday
29. Friday
30. Tuesday
31. D
32. A
33. B
34. C
35. A
36. C
37. D
38. B
39. 567, 576, 657, 675, 756, 765
40. 198

Paper 10

1 156
2 322
3 5736, 6537, 6573, 7536
4 1
5 4
6 9
7 14
8 3459
9 three thousand four hundred and fifty-nine
10 9543
11 nine thousand five hundred and forty-three
12 15 689
13 fifteen thousand six hundred and eighty-nine
14 98 651
15 ninety eight thousand six hundred and fifty-one
16 1489
17 7089
18 school stories
19 books on hobbies
20 310
21 mysteries
22 10
23 50
24 £4
25 £26
26 £2.67
27 £1.35
28 even
29 even
30 even
31 odd
32 10
33 12
34 5
35 $\frac{1}{4}$
36 $\frac{3}{4}$
37 $\frac{1}{5}$
38 $\frac{4}{5}$
39 $\frac{2}{3}$
40 $\frac{1}{3}$

Paper 11

1 9 min
2 41
3 362
4 6
5 2
6 3
7 3
8 4
9 1058
10 1632
11 11
12 564
13 2020
14 7
15 A
16 C
17 D
18 4
19 800
20 40
21 4
22 8
23 600
24 160
25 36
26 6
27 5
28 5
29 fast
30 10
31 slow
32 20
33 slow
34 11:10
35 12:40
36 14:00
37 15:05
38 16:20
39 − +
40 + −

Paper 12

1 3:07 p.m.
2 11:45 p.m.
3 10:51
4–5 A and D
6 £24.20
7 £1.50
8 £1.75
9 £61.70
10 £34.00

11

12

13

14

15 09:30
16 10:00
17 10:00
18 10:30
19 10:30
20 10:45
21 10:45
22 11:15
23 11:15
24 11:45
25 11:45
26 12:15
27 A − iii
28 B − i
29 C − ii
30 D − iv
31 150 ml
32 62
33 10
34 group A
35 8
36 £930
37 37
38 25
39 3
40 4

Paper 13

1–2 1, 2
3–4 1, 3
5–6 2, 3 or 1, 4
7–8 1, 4 or 2, 3
9–10 1, 5 or 2, 4
11–12 2, 4 or 1, 5
13–14 3, 4
15–18

19–23

24 + × or ÷ −
25 + ×
26 − + or ÷ ×
27 − −
28 − + or ÷ −
29 + +
30 24
31 7
32 3
33 1
34 £14.40
35 21
36 Mr Bell
37 Mr Eliot
38 Mr Dring
39 5.4 kg
40 7.4 kg

Paper 14

1 95
2 90
3 43
4 47
5 523
6 518
7 237
8 243
9 110
10 121
11 14
12 132
13 20
14 12
15 30 min
16 2800
17 201
18 11:04
19 13
20 180
21 28 210
22 600
23 406
24 6000
25 460
26 10
27 54 m
28 978
29 1000
30 96
31 105
32 90
33 144
34 7
35 12
36 6
37 10 cm or 0.1 m
38 25
39 2000
40 500

Paper 15

1 −20
2 −18
3 4
4 1 cm
5 2 cm
6 3 cm
7 1.5 cm or 15 mm
8 1.5 cm or 15 mm
9 7 cm
10 5 cm
11 2 cm
12 200
13 200
14 390
15 B
16 C
17 E
18 126
19 4
20 18
21 27
22 13
23 16
24 5
25 11
26 14
27 73
28 10
29 fast
30 20
31 slow
32 20
33 fast
34 30
35 slow
36 600
37 30
38 86 552
39 eighty-six thousand five hundred and fifty-two
40 4120

Paper 16

1 $\frac{1}{2}$
2 $\frac{3}{6}$
3 $\frac{6}{12}$
4 $\frac{1}{3}$
5 $\frac{2}{6}$
6 $\frac{1}{2}$
7 $\frac{1}{4}$
8 $\frac{1}{10}$
9 6.50
10 Brighton
11 Cambridge
12 27 km
13 95 km
14 250 km
15 150 km
16 8018

17

18

19

20 13
21 14
22 12
23 4.80   24 5.10
25 4   26 76.5
27 1.5   28 79.2
29 30   30 0
31 5   32 9
33 13   34 10 m
35 16.04 m   36 2.55 m
37 3.40 m   38 £1.20
39 £13.20   40 5

Paper 17

1 61
2 61
3 60
4 3
5 4
6 1000
7 $\frac{1}{8}$
8 $\frac{1}{2}$
9 $\frac{1}{8}$
10 $\frac{1}{4}$
11 66
12 42
13 £5.50
14 +
15 +
16 +
17 ×
18 +
19 −
20 ×
21 ×
22 ×
23 +
24 ÷
25 ÷
26 ×
27 −
28 × or ÷
29 −
30 2996
31 19.74
32 22.68
33 3
34 8
35 2
36 12
37 4
38 6
39 10
40 2

Paper 18

1 £0.75 or 75p
2 £0.50 or 50p
3 54p
4 60p
5 2055
6 2065
7 $2\frac{1}{2}$
8 3
9 8 hr
10 4 hr
11 164
12 172
13 41.1
14 63
15 82.7
16 3
17 6
18 30
19 4
20 6
21 5   22 6.55
23 3.45   24 640
25 84   26 56
27 84   28 64
29 92   30 9
31 6   32 7
33 25   34 31
35 137   36 10
37 7

38

39

40

Paper 19

1 £0.02
2 £2.22
3 622
4 642
5 10
6 9.64
7 3440
8 9
9 24 m
10 36 m^2
11 30
12 20
13 35
14 45
15 35
16 2 hr 45 min
17 300
18 600
19 150
20 200
21 −3
22 −14 °C, −1 °C, 5 °C
23 11 + 2
24 19 − 6
25 10 − 3$\frac{1}{2}$
26 4$\frac{1}{4}$ + 2$\frac{1}{4}$
27 18 − 13
28 5 × 1
29 231
30 5672
31 56 720
32 60
33 115
34 40
35 £700
36 350
37 49
38 281
39 49
40 881

Paper 20

1 3
2 18
3 35
4 8
5 10
6 10:13
7 20
8 30
9 57
10 55
11 Deborah
12 Stuart
13 Stuart
14 Deborah
15 Mark
16 Andrea
17 Mark
18 Alison
19 10
20 10
21 16
22 76
23 128.25
24 136.25
25 E
26 C
27 E
28 B
29 12
30 8$\frac{1}{2}$ l
31 10 July
32 21st
33 3
34 11 July
35 6
36 10$\frac{1}{2}$
37 123
38 131
39 27
40 24

Paper 21

1 17:00
2 23:00
3 21:05
4 16:22
5 14:51
6 18:30
7 08:45
8 10:10
9 1
10 240
11 500
12 60
13 200 seconds
14 400
15 11
16–21

×	10	11	12
2	20	**(22)**	24
3	**(30)**	33	**(36)**
4	**(40)**	44	48
5	50	**(55)**	**(60)**

22 1474
23 10 030
24 6002
25 2
26 36
27 54
28 72
29 A
30 C
31 D
32 6
33 3
34 425
35 −9 °C
36 −31 °C
37 1452
38 5412
39 4682
40 8642

Paper 22

1 16
2 13
3 10
4 12
5 $11\frac{1}{2}$
6 $19\frac{1}{2}$
7 $27\frac{1}{2}$
8 E
9 SE
10 N
11 NW
12 NW
13 SE
14 5
15 280
16 68
17 10
18 5
19 45
20 56
21 120
22 140
23 11
24 8
25 $\frac{1}{6}$
26 $\frac{5}{6}$
27 $\frac{1}{2}$ or $\frac{3}{6}$
28 $\frac{1}{2}$ or $\frac{3}{6}$
29 $\frac{1}{8}$
30 $\frac{7}{8}$

31–35

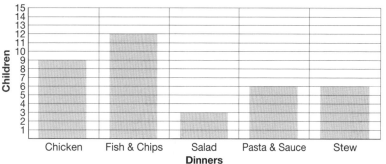

36 fish and chips
37 salad
38 9204
39 5075
40 140

Paper 23

1 40
2 900
3 0
4 63, 74
5 17, $19\frac{1}{2}$
6 11, 7
7 13
8 21
9 £4.90
10 £2.60
11 £5.80
12 £3.70
13 £5.20
14 £5.10
15 £9.40
16 69
17 405
18 3
19 237
20 852
21 equilateral triangle
22 quadrilateral
23 cube
24 isosceles triangle
25 semicircle
26 pentagon
27 tetrahedron
28 hexagon
29 heptagon
30 quadrilateral
31 parallelogram
32 hexagon
33 cube
34 100
35 3521
36 3512
37 2531
38 2513
39 1532
40 1523

Paper 24

1 57
2 74
3 Beechton
4 47
5 Applegate
6 49
7 248
8 27
9 748
10 227
11 368
12 968
13 52
14 552
15 pentagon
16 0
17 heptagon
18 $8\frac{1}{2}$
19 10
20 36
21 45
22 42
23 22
24 5p
25 11p
26 10:10
27 10:10
28 10:40
29 10:40
30 11:00
31 11:00
32 11:30
33 11:30
34 12:00
35 4
36 B
37 C
38 250
39 3
40 3276

Paper 12

1 It is now 2:37 p.m. In half an hour's time it will be __3__ : __07__ p.m.

2 What time is a quarter of an hour before midnight? __11__ : __45__ p.m.

3 Six minutes after 10:45 is __10__ : __51__

£11.50	£13.25	£12.75	£11.25	£12.95
A	B	C	D	E

4–5 Which two toys could you buy with £23.00? __A__ and __D__

6 How much would it cost to buy the bat and the football? £ __24.20__

7 How much change would you have from £13.00
if you bought a van (A)? £ __1.50__

8 How much change would you have from £15.00
if you bought a boat (B)? £ __1.75__

9 How much would it cost to buy all the toys? £ __61.85__

10 How much would it cost to buy a van and two bats? £ __34.00__

11–14 Draw the lines of **symmetry** in each of the following shapes.

The first one has been done for you.

31

Handwritten working (right margin):

22.50
+11.50
34.00

11.25
+12.95
£24.20

③ 3

4 9
18.00
−13.25
1.75

24.20
+13.25
37.45

⑤ 7

37.45
+11.25
48.70

48.70
+12.95
61.65

4

15–26 The table below should show the important times in the morning at Greenway Primary School.

Each lesson is half an hour long. Break lasts 15 minutes. Lessons begin at 09:30.

Fill in the correct times.

	Begins	Ends
First lesson	9:30	10:00
Second lesson	10:00	10:30
Break	10:30	10:45
Third lesson	10:45	11:15
Fourth lesson	11:15	11:45
Fifth lesson	11:45	12:15

12 12

27–30 Join each three-dimensional object on the left with its **net** on the right by drawing a line.

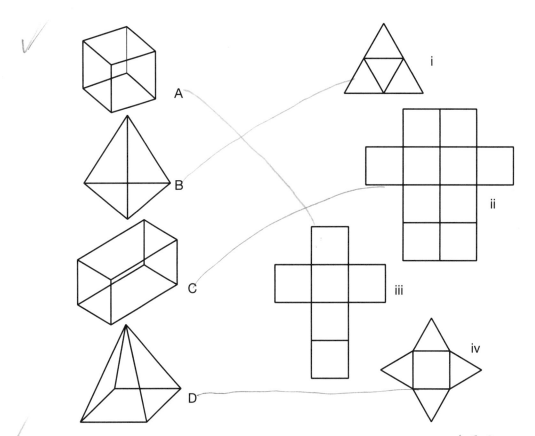

4 4

31 What is the difference between 1 litre and 850 ml? _150_ ml

1 1

32

The children in a swimming club made this **pictogram**.

It shows how many children of each age group could swim.

Age 7	🏃 🏃								
Age 8	🏃 🏃 🏃 🏃								
Age 9	🏃 🏃 🏃 🏃 🏃 🏃 🏃 🏃								
Age 10	🏃 🏃 🏃 🏃 🏃 🏃 🏃 🏃 🏃								
Age 11	🏃 🏃 🏃 🏃 🏃 🏃 🏃 🏃 🏃								

Key

🏃 = 2 children

🏃 = 1 child

32 How many children in the club can swim? _____62_____

33 How many more 10-year-olds than 8-year-olds can swim? ___10___

Swimming group A has all the 10-year-olds and 11-year-olds.

Swimming group B has all the younger children.

34 Which is the larger group? ___A___

35 How many more are in this group? ___8___

A season ticket for the swimming baths costs £15.00 each.

36 If all the children bought a season ticket, what would be the total cost? ___1346___

Last Thursday there was a 100 m race. Two of the 9-year-olds entered along with all the 10- and 11-year-olds.

37 How many were in the race? ___37___

38 The rest of the children entered the 50 m race. How many were in this race? ___25___   ⑥ 7

39 What is the remainder when 28 is divided by 5? ___3___

40 What is the remainder when 28 is divided by 6? ___4___   ② 2

Now go to the Progress Chart to record your score!   Total ( ) 40

33

Paper 13

Use two of the numbers in the brackets to complete the following **sums**. Do not use the same combination twice.

1–2 _2_ + _1_ + 9 = 12   (1, 2, 3, 4, 5, 6, 7, 8)

3–4 _3_ + _1_ + 8 = 12   (1, 2, 3, 4, 5, 6, 7)

5–6 _4_ + _1_ + 7 = 12   (1, 2, 3, 4, 5, 6)

7–8 _3_ + _2_ + 7 = 12   (1, 2, 3, 4, 5, 6)

9–10 _4_ + _2_ + 6 = 12   (1, 2, 3, 4, 5)

11–12 _5_ + _1_ + 6 = 12   (1, 2, 3, 4, 5)

13–14 _3_ + _4_ + 5 = 12   (1, 2, 3, 4)

14

15–18 Use the numbers in the brackets below only once to make each side of the square add up to 12. You can use the **sums** above to help you.

(1, 2, 3, 5)

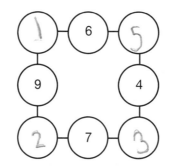

4

19–23 Make these shapes look the same on each side of the **mirror line**.

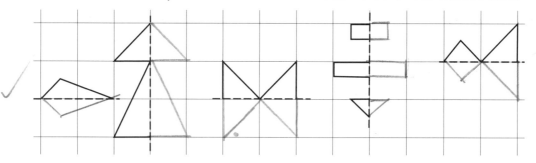

5

Put a sign in each space so that each question will be correct.

24 6 _+_ 6 = 4 _×_ 3

25 4 _+_ 5 = 3 _×_ 3

26 6 _−_ 2 = 3 _+_ 1

34

27 7 _−_ 4 = 4 _−_ 1

28 8 _÷_ 2 = 5 _+_ 1

29 7 _+_ 1 = 4 _+_ 4

make your signs much clearer!

This bar chart shows how many people got on a bus at each of the four stops in the centre of the town.

7   3   10   4

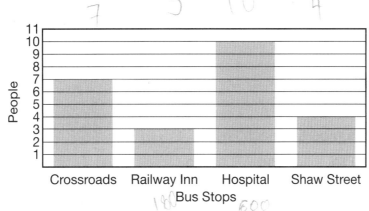

30 How many people got on the bus altogether? _24_

31 How many more people got on at the hospital than at the Railway Inn? _7_

32 How many more people got on at the crossroads than at Shaw Street? _3_

33 How many more people got on at Shaw Street than at the Railway Inn? _1_

34 If all the people who got on the bus paid 60p each, how much was this altogether? £ _____

7.80
6.60
14.40

A quarter of the passengers got off the bus at the next stop and 3 more got on.

35 Now how many passengers would be on the bus? _21_

Mrs Andrews 18 kg

Mr Bell 8.6 kg

Mrs Clark 17.1 kg

Mr Dring 21.4 kg

Mr Eliot 14.8 kg

Passengers cannot take more than 16 kg on the plane.

35

36–37 Who was allowed to take all their luggage with them?

MR BELL and _MR ELIOT_

38 Whose luggage is the heaviest?

MR DRING

39 How much over 16 kg is his case?

_4.4 KG_

40 How much extra weight would Mr Bell be allowed to put in his case to make it up to 16 kg?

_7.4 KG_   4 5

Now go to the Progress Chart to record your score!   Total   40

Paper 14

Write the next two numbers in each line.

1–2	115	110	105	100	_95_	_90_
3–4	27	31	35	39	_43_	_47_
5–6	543	538	533	528	_523_ ✓	_513_ ✗
7–8	213	219	225	231	_237_	_243_
9–10	66	77	88	99	_110_	_121_

9 10

11 How many times can I take 7 from 98? –ALOT!   _14_   1

NOT SO MANY ↲

Underline the correct answer in each line.

12 12 × 11 = 112   121   123   <u>132</u>   144

13 400 ÷ 20 = 40   <u>20</u>   200   400   4

14 101 – 89 = <u>12</u>   11   21   23   22

15 $\frac{1}{2}$ hour = 15 min   20 min   <u>30 min</u>   40 min   45 min

16 70 × 40 = 280   <u>2800</u>   1100   240   470

17 603 ÷ 3 = 21   31   301   <u>201</u>   210

6 6

$$3\overline{)603} \quad 201$$

18 My watch is 9 minutes slow. It shows 5 minutes to 11. What is the right time?   _4 : 58_

19 When a number is taken away from 21 the answer is 8. What is the number?   _13_   1 2

36

20
27
68
49
+ 36
―――
180
3

21   403
✗   × 70
―――――
2800

| A | ↕ 3 m |

←――――― 200 m ―――――→

✓ **22** What is the **area** of rectangle A? _600_ m²

✓ **23** What is the **perimeter** of rectangle A? _406_ m

| B | ↕ 30 m |

←――――― 200 m ―――――→

✓ **24** What is the **area** of rectangle B? _6000_ m²

✓ **25** What is the **perimeter** of rectangle B? _460_ m

✓ **26** How many times bigger is the **area** of rectangle B than the **area** of rectangle A?   _10_

✗ **27** By how much is the **perimeter** of B bigger than the **perimeter** of A?   _60 m_   ⑤ ⑥

✓ **28** From the **digits** 7, 8 and 9 make a number so that 9 is the hundred and 8 is the unit.   _978_

✗ **29** What is the **product** of 10 and 100?   _10_   ① ②

Write the answers to the following questions.

✓ **30** $12 \times 8 = 10 \times 8 + 2 \times 8 =$ _96_

✓ **31** $15 \times 7 = 10 \times 7 + 5 \times 7 =$ _105_

✓ **32** $18 \times 5 = 10 \times 5 + 8 \times 5 =$ _90_

✓ **33** $16 \times 9 = 10 \times 9 + 6 \times 9 =$ _144_

④ ④

My brother has 40 counters.

18 are yellow, 15 are green and the rest are blue.

✓ **34** How many are blue? _7_

✓ **35** How many times can I take 6 from 72? _12_ (2) 2

To make a rosette you need 15 cm of ribbon.

✗ **36** How many could you make with a metre of ribbon? _15_

✗ **37** How much ribbon would be left over? _5 cm_ (0) 2

✓ **38** What is the **sum** of the odd numbers smaller than 10? _25_ (1) 1

✓ **39** What needs to be added to change 5864 to 7864? _2000_

✓ **40** What needs to be subtracted to change 6842 to 6342? _500_ (2) 2

Now go to the Progress Chart to record your score! **Total** ◯ 40

Paper 15

1–2 Fill in the missing numbers on this number line.

-22   -21   _____   -19   _____   -17   -16   ◯ 2

3 How many weeks are there in 28 days? _____ ◯ 1

Here is part of a centimetre ruler.

A   B C D   E F G   H I J   K

19   20   21   22   23   24   25   26   27   28

4 How far is it from A to B? _____

5 How far is it from D to G? _____

6 How far is it from G to K? _____

7 How far is it from F to H? _____

8 What is the distance between A and C? _____

9 How far is it from A to K? _____

10 How far is it from B to J? _____

11 What is the distance from C to F? _____ ◯ 8

12 The film lasted 153 min, which is _____ min to the nearest 100 min.

13 Oxton to Cowster is 197 miles, which is _____ miles to the nearest 10 miles.

14 The return trip (from Oxton to Cowster and back) is _____ miles to the nearest 10 miles. ◯ 3

A   B   C   D   E

15–17 Shade in the **quadrilaterals**. ◯ 3

18 What is the **product** of 6 and 21? _____

You start with 16 eggs. Half are broken so you throw them away. Half of the unbroken eggs are too old so you throw them away.

19 You are now left with _____ good eggs.

20 Twice nine is _____ ◯ 3

Our class

Black shoes   11   5   8   Grey socks

3

21 How many children are in the class? _____

22 How many children are wearing grey socks? _____

23 How many are wearing black shoes? _____

24 _____ children are wearing grey socks and black shoes.

25 How many children are not wearing black shoes?   _____

26 _____ are not wearing grey socks.

27 I spend 27p. What change should I receive if I give
the shopkeeper £1.00?   _____ p

The time is 5 to 8. How fast or slow are these clocks?

Write the number of minutes and ring the correct word for each clock

28–29 _____ minutes   fast

slow

30–31 _____ minutes   fast

slow

32–33 _____ minutes   fast

slow

34–35 _____ minutes   fast

slow

36 What needs to be added/subtracted to change 7812 to 7212?

_____

37 What needs to be added/subtracted to change 6324 to 6354?

_____

38 What is the largest number you can make with these **digits**:
2, 5, 8, 6, 5?   _____

39 Now write it in words.

_____

40 Write in figures four thousand, one hundred and twenty.   _____

Now go to the Progress Chart to record your score!   Total   40

Paper 16

1–3 What fraction of the board is shaded? Underline the correct answers.

$\frac{1}{2}$ $\frac{1}{3}$ $\frac{1}{6}$ $\frac{1}{12}$ $\frac{2}{3}$ $\frac{2}{6}$ $\frac{2}{12}$ $\frac{3}{6}$ $\frac{3}{12}$ $\frac{6}{12}$

4–5 What fraction of the paperclips has been ringed? Underline all the correct answers.

$\frac{1}{2}$ $\frac{1}{3}$ $\frac{1}{4}$ $\frac{1}{6}$ $\frac{2}{3}$ $\frac{2}{4}$ $\frac{2}{6}$ $\frac{3}{4}$ $\frac{3}{6}$

6 Which fraction is larger: $\frac{1}{2}$ or $\frac{1}{4}$?   _____   **6**

Put a circle round the correct answer.

7 $0.25 =$ $\frac{1}{2}$ $\frac{2}{5}$ $\frac{1}{4}$ $\frac{25}{10}$

8 $0.1 =$ $\frac{1}{2}$ $\frac{1}{1}$ $\frac{1}{10}$ $\frac{1}{100}$ **2**

9 In a sponsored swim, Kevin's dad says he will pay 50p per length.

Kevin swims 13 lengths, so his dad has to pay   £ _____   **1**

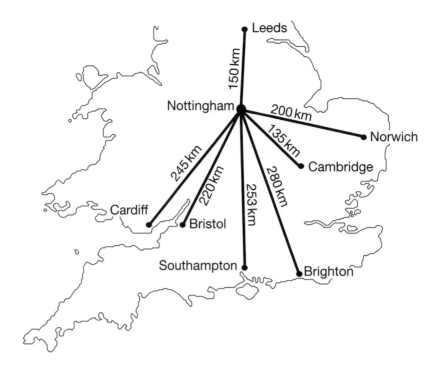

10 Which town is furthest away from Nottingham? _____

11 Which town is nearest to Nottingham? _____

12 Brighton is further away from Nottingham than
    Southampton is by _____

13 Cardiff is further away from Nottingham than Leeds is by _____

14 What is the distance from Nottingham to Southampton
    to the nearest 10 km? _____ km

15 What is the distance from Nottingham to Leeds
    to the nearest 10 km? _____ km   6

16 Write in figures: eight thousand and eighteen. _____   1

17–19 Carefully draw the hands on the clocks on the right so they show the
       same times as those on the left.

12:30

Remember that the
hour hand is shorter
than the minute hand.

○ 3

20 $\frac{1}{2}$ of 26 = _____

21 $\frac{2}{3}$ of 21 = _____

22 $\frac{3}{4}$ of 16 = _____

○ 3

23 6 paper chains at 80p cost £_____ .

24 6 strands of tinsel at 85p cost £_____ .

25 How many Christmas cards, at 45p can I buy with £2.00?   _____ ○ 3

Alison weighs 39 kg, Christopher weighs 37.5 kg and Rachel weighs 41.7 kg.

26 Alison and Christopher together weigh   _____ kg

27 How much heavier is Alison than Christopher?   _____ kg

28 Christopher and Rachel together weigh   _____ kg   ○ 3

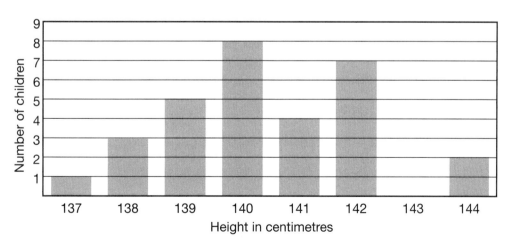

29 How many children are shown on the bar chart?   _____

30 How many children are 143 cm tall? _____

31 How many more children are 140 cm tall than are 138 cm? _____

32 How many children are less than 140 cm tall? _____

33 How many children are more than 140 cm tall? _____ ◯ 5

34 4 m 25 cm + 5 m 75 cm = _____ m

35 8 m 36 cm + 7 m 68 cm = _____ m

36 5 m 0 cm − 2 m 45 cm = _____ m

37 6 m 10 cm − 2 m 70 cm = _____ m ◯ 4

38–39 If 5 m of material costs £6.00, 1 m will cost _____
and 11 m will cost _____. ◯ 2

40 How many $\frac{1}{2}$ hour lessons are there between 09:30 and 12:00? _____ ◯ 1

Now go to the Progress Chart to record your score!   Total ◯ 40

Paper 17

Thirty days has September,
April, June and November.
All the rest have 31,
Except February alone
Which has but 28 days clear,
And 29 in each leap year.

1 In June and July together there are _____ days.

2 In March and April together there are _____ days.

3 In February and March together, in a leap year, there are _____ days.

4 When it is not a leap year, how many more days are in
December than February? _____

5 How many years are there in 48 months? _____

6 How many years in a millennium? _____ ◯ 6

7 What fraction of the picture above is dotted? _____

8 What fraction is striped? _____

9 What fraction is plain? _____

10 What fraction has crosses? _____ ◯ 4

11 If three pencils cost 99p what will be the cost of two pencils? _____ p

12 What is the **product** of 7 and 6? _____

13 If 12 books cost £66.00 what is the cost of one book? _____ ◯ 3

Put a sign in each space so that each question will be correct.

14–15 7 ___ 1 = 4 ___ 4

16–17 3 ___ 7 = 5 ___ 2

18–19 6 ___ 1 = 8 ___ 1

20–21 6 ___ 4 = 2 ___ 12

22–23 4 ___ 4 = 10 ___ 6

24–25 12 ___ 3 = 8 ___ 2

26–27 2 ___ 7 = 15 ___ 1

28–29 3 ___ 1 = 7 ___ 4 ◯ 16

30   428
    × 7
   _____

31   3.29
    × 6
   _____

32   3.24
    × 7
   _____ ◯ 3

This diagram shows that one whole can be divided into thirds, sixths and twelfths.

1 Whole											
$\frac{1}{3}$				$\frac{1}{3}$				$\frac{1}{3}$			
$\frac{1}{6}$		$\frac{1}{6}$		$\frac{1}{6}$		$\frac{1}{6}$		$\frac{1}{6}$		$\frac{1}{6}$	
$\frac{1}{12}$	$\frac{1}{12}$	$\frac{1}{12}$	$\frac{1}{12}$	$\frac{1}{12}$	$\frac{1}{12}$	$\frac{1}{12}$	$\frac{1}{12}$	$\frac{1}{12}$	$\frac{1}{12}$	$\frac{1}{12}$	$\frac{1}{12}$

33 How many $\frac{1}{3}$s make 1? _____

34 How many $\frac{1}{12}$s make $\frac{2}{3}$? _____

35 How many $\frac{1}{6}$s make $\frac{1}{3}$? _____

36 How many $\frac{1}{12}$s make 1? _____

37 How many $\frac{1}{6}$s make $\frac{2}{3}$? _____

38 How many $\frac{1}{6}$s make 1? _____

39 How many $\frac{1}{12}$s make $\frac{5}{6}$? _____

40 How many $\frac{1}{3}$s make $\frac{8}{12}$? _____ ⬤ 8

Now go to the Progress Chart to record your score! Total ⬤ 40

Paper 18

Write the next two numbers in each of the following lines.

1–2	£1.75	£1.50	£1.25	£1.00	_____	_____
3–4	30p	36p	42p	48p	_____	_____
5–6	2015	2025	2035	2045	_____	_____
7–8	$\frac{1}{2}$	1	$1\frac{1}{2}$	2	_____	_____
9–10	1 day	20 hr	16 hr	12 hr	_____	_____
11–12	132	140	148	156	_____	_____

⬤ 12

46

13	22.5	14	26.5	15	38.9
	+18.6		+ 36.5		+ 43.8

⬤ 3

Fill in the missing numbers in each of these questions.

16 4 × _____ = 12

17 2 + 3 + _____ = 11

18 5 × 6 = _____

19 12 – _____ = 8

20 24 + _____ = 30

⬤ 5

21 How many years in 60 months? _____

⬤ 1

Eve bought a book for £4.75 and some writing paper for £1.80.

22 How much did she spend? £_____

23 How much change would she have from £10.00? £_____

⬤ 2

24 The school hall has 32 rows of chairs and there are 20 chairs in each row. How many chairs are there altogether? _____

25 What is the **product** of 7 and 12? _____

⬤ 2

26–29   × 4 →

14	
21	
16	
23	

30–34   ÷ 6 →

54	
36	
42	
150	
186	

⬤ 9

35 How many erasers for 5p each could you buy with £6.85? _____

36 50 × 1 = 60 – _____

37 20 × 0 = 7 – _____

⬤ 3

Put the hands on these clocks.

38 25 past 2

39 $\frac{1}{4}$ to 10

40 10 past 7

◯ 3

Now go to the Progress Chart to record your score! Total ◯ 40

Paper 19

1–2 Underline the smallest and circle the largest.

22p, £2, £0.02, £2.22, £2.02 202p

3–4 Underline the smallest and circle the largest.

623 632 642 640 622 624

◯ 4

5 **Round** to the nearest pound: £9.66 = £_____

6 Write 964p in £. 964p = £_____

7 Write metres in centimetres: 34.4 m = _____ cm

◯ 3

8 The age of Bridget, Bob and Sarah add up to 24 years.

If Bob is 8 and Bridget is 7, how old is Sarah? _____

◯ 1

One side of a **square** room is 6 m.

9 How far is it all round? _____

10 What is the **area** of the **square** floor? _____

◯ 2

Here is a timetable for Wednesday morning.

Mathematics	09:15–09:45
Music	09:45–10:30
Break	10:30–10:50
History	10:50–11:25
Games	11:25–12:00

11 We do mathematics for _____ min.

12 Break is _____ min long.

13 We play games for _____ min.

14 We spend _____ min having our music lesson.

15 How long is the history lesson? _____ min.

16 From 09:15 to 12:00 is _____ hour _____ min.   ⬤ 6

17 London to Leeds is 283 miles, which is _____ miles
    to the nearest 100 miles.

18 The return trip (to Leeds and back) is _____ miles
    to the nearest 100 miles.   ⬤ 2

19–20 The fuel tank in a truck holds 151 litres, which is _____ litres
    to the nearest 10 litres and _____ litres to the nearest 100 litres.   ⬤ 2

21 Fill in the missing number in the brackets on this number line.

        -5   (___)   1   ⬤ 1

22 Put these temperatures in order, lowest first.

    5 °C   -14 °C   -1 °C   _____ _____ _____   ⬤ 1

Underline the two questions in each line which give the answer.

23–24 $13 =$ $9 + 3$ 7×2 $11 + 2$ $19 - 6$ $14 + 1$

25–26 $6\frac{1}{2} =$ $12\frac{1}{2} - 6\frac{1}{2}$ $10 - 3\frac{1}{2}$ $4 + 2$ $5\frac{1}{4} + 2\frac{1}{4}$ $4\frac{1}{4} + 2\frac{1}{4}$

27–28 $5 =$ $10 - 10$ 20×5 $18 - 13$ $15 - 5$ 5×1 ⬤ 6

29	88	30	709	31	709
	77		× 8		× 80
	+ 66		———		———
	———				

3

Here is a **pictogram** which shows the number of people who had tea at Meg's Café last Thursday.

 represents 5 people having tea.

2pm–3pm	
3pm–4pm	
4pm–5pm	
5pm–6pm	

32 How many people had tea at Meg's Café between 2 p.m. and 4 p.m.? _____

33 How many had tea between 4 p.m. and 6 p.m.? _____

34 How many more people had tea between 4 p.m. and 5 p.m., than between 2 p.m. and 3 p.m.? _____

35 If the café charged £4 for a tea how much money was taken last Thursday? _____

Twice the number of people who had tea at Meg's Café on Thursday had tea there on Saturday.

36 How many were there on Saturday? _____

5

Look at this **sum** carefully.

        32 + 49   = 81

Now use it to help you with the following questions.

37 81 – 32   = _____   38 132 + 149 = _____

39 181 – 132 = _____   40 532 + 349 = _____

4

Now go to the Progress Chart to record your score!   Total   40

50

Paper 20

Fill in the missing numbers so that each question will be correct.

1	2	3
2 _ + 46 ――― 69	40 ― __ ―― 22	__ × 3 ―― 105

3

4 Rakesh gets £2.50 pocket money a week.

If he saves half of it, how long will it take him to save
£10.00?   _____ weeks

5 How many times can I take 20 from 200?   _____

6 A clock is 12 minutes fast. What is the correct time
when the clock shows 10:25?   ____ : ____

7 Find the **sum** of all the even numbers between 1 and 9.   _____

4

8 There are 85 children in Classes 1, 2 and 3. If there are 28 in
Class 1, and 27 in Class 2, how many are there in Class 3? _____

9 How many are there in Classes 2 and 3 together?   _____

10 How many are there in Classes 1 and 2 together?   _____

3

Here are the marks some children got in the last three spelling tests
(out of 10).

	Andrea	Mark	Deborah	Stuart	Alison	Steven
Test 1	7	8	9	7	8	9
Test 2	4	6	8	5	7	6
Test 3	9	10	8	7	9	7
Totals						

11 Who had the highest total marks?   _____

12 Who had the lowest total marks?   _____

13 Who got fewer than 8 marks in each of the tests?   _____

14 Who got 8 or more marks in each of the tests? _____

15 Who got 10 in one test? _____

16 Who had fewer than 5 marks in one test? _____

17–18 _____ and _____ got the same total marks.

Look at the **pictogram** and answer the questions.

Roundabouts	☺☺☺☺☺☺☺☺☺
Scenic Railway	☺☺☺☺☺☺☺☺
Dodgems	☺☺☺☺☺☺☺☺☺☺☺
Swing-boats	☺☺☺☺☺☺
Go Karts	☺☺☺☺

Key

☺ represents
2 people

19 How many more children went on the dodgems than on the swing-boats? ____

20 There were ____ fewer children on the go karts than on the roundabouts.

21 How many children went on the scenic railway? ____

22 What was the total number of children who went on these amusements? ____

Maria is 131.5 cm tall. Susan is 3.25 cm shorter than Maria.
Cathy is 4.75 cm taller than Maria.

23 How tall is Susan? _____ cm

24 How tall is Cathy? _____ cm

A   B   C   D   E

25–26 Jug _____ holds the most and jug _____ holds the least.

27–28 Jug _____ holds exactly twice as much as jug _____.

29 A beaker holds $\frac{1}{8}$ litre. How many beakers full of water can be poured from jug A? _____

30 What is the total amount that all the jugs will hold? _____   **6**

July					
Sunday		5	12	19	26
Monday		6	13	20	27
Tuesday		7	14	21	28
Wednesday	1	8	15	22	29
Thursday	2	9	16	23	30
Friday	3	10	17	24	31
Saturday	4	11	18	25	

31 If today's date is July 3rd, what will be the date in one week's time? _____

32 What is the date on the third Tuesday in July? _____

33 How many days appear 5 times in this July? _____

34 A fortnight before July 25th is _____   **4**

Fill in the missing numbers in each line.

35–36 $1\frac{1}{2}$ 3 $4\frac{1}{2}$ _____ $7\frac{1}{2}$ 9   _____   12

37–38   115   119   _____   127   _____   135   139

39–40   36   33   30   _____   _____   21   18   **6**

Paper 21

Write these times for the 24-hour clock.

1 5 p.m. ___ : ___

2 11 p.m. ___ : ___

3 9:05 p.m. ___ : ___

4 4:22 p.m. ___ : ___

5 2:51 p.m. ___ : ___

6 6:30 p.m. ___ : ___

7 8:45 a.m. ___ : ___

8 10:10 a.m. ___ : ___

  8

9 What number needs to go in the box?

2341 = 2000 + 300 + 40 + [ ]

1

10 A ladder is 236 cm long, which is ___ cm to the nearest 10 cm.

11 Two ladders are ___ cm to the nearest 100 cm.

2

12 A chocolate biscuit lasts Amy 55 seconds, which is ___ seconds to the nearest 10 seconds.

13 How long will it take her to eat 4 at the same speed, to the nearest 100 seconds? ___

2

14 What needs to be added/subtracted to change 8621 to 8221? ___

15 What number will divide 33 and 44? ___

2

16–21 Here is part of a tables chart. Complete the empty brackets.

×			
	20	( )	24
	( )	33	( )
	( )	44	48
	50	( )	( )

6

22 How many pence in £14.74? ___

23 How many pence in £100.30? ___

24 How many pence in £60.02? ___

25 How many pence in £0.02? ___

4

26–28 Which of these numbers are exactly **divisible** by 9? Underline them.

15   24   36   46   54   62   72   84   95   98   107

○ 3

29–31 Colour in any **octagons** below.

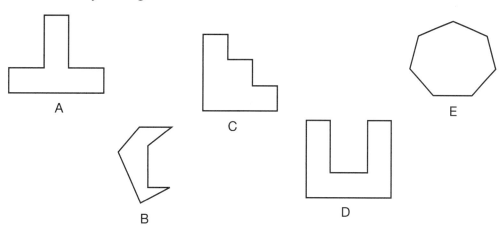

A

C

E

B

D

32 Tickets for a concert cost £9.
How many tickets can I buy with £60?

_____

○ 3

Twenty-five children are going to a swimming pool by a minibus which can take 11 passengers.

33 How many trips must the minibus make?

_____

○ 2

34 Write the correct number in the box.

450    $\xrightarrow{\text{25 less is}}$ [   ]

○ 1

35 Draw a circle around the lowest temperature: −7 °C   −9 °C

36 Draw a circle around the lowest temperature: −31 °C   −30 °C

○ 2

Put a ring round the smallest and underline the largest in each line.

37–38   5412   1452   4251   2415   2514   5214

39–40   8426   4862   6824   8642   6842   4682

○ 4

Now go to the Progress Chart to record your score!   Total ○ 40

55

Paper 22

Fill in the missing numbers in each line.

1–2	34	28	23	19	___	14	___
3–4	___	9	11	10	12	11	13	___
5–7	$3\frac{1}{2}$	$7\frac{1}{2}$	___	$15\frac{1}{2}$	___	$23\frac{1}{2}$	___

7

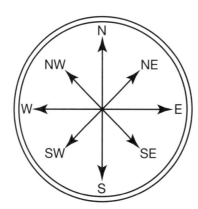

Can you name these compass points?

8 90° clockwise from N is _____

9 90° anticlockwise from SW is _____

10 2 right-angles clockwise from S is _____

11 3 right-angles anticlockwise from SW is _____

12 2 right-angles anticlockwise from SE is _____

13 2 right-angles clockwise from NW is _____

6

14 If a goldfish costs £1.25, how many can I buy for £6.25? _____

1

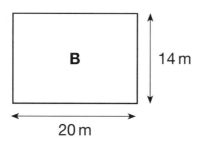

15 What is the **area** of rectangle B? _____ m²

16 What is the **perimeter** of rectangle B? _____ m

2

Complete the following lines.

17–18	80	40	20	_____	_____
19–20	12	23	34	_____	_____
21–22	60	80	100	_____	_____
23–24	20	17	14	_____	_____

Write the correct fraction in its lowest form in each space.

25 Dotted _____

26 White _____

27 Dotted _____

28 White _____

29 Dotted _____

30 White _____

31–35 A class of 36 children voted for their favourite school dinners and then made a chart.

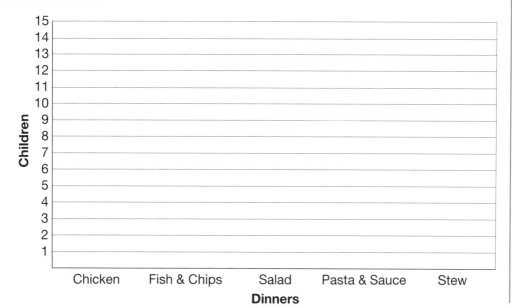

Shade in the columns to show how they voted:

- 3 children voted for salad.

- 3 times as many voted for chicken.

- One third of the class voted for fish and chips.

- The number who voted for stew was one half of the number who voted for fish and chips.

- Both sets of twins in the class, plus two other children, voted for pasta and sauce.

36 The most popular school dinner was _____

37 The least popular school dinner was _____ ⃝ 7

38 Write in figures nine thousand, two hundred and four. _____

39 Write in figures five thousand and seventy-five. _____

40 The TV programme lasted 138 minutes, which is _____ min to the nearest 10 min. ⃝ 3

Now go to the Progress Chart to record your score!   Total ⃝ 40

Paper 23

What number needs to go in the box?

1 $5842 = 5000 + 800 +$ ⬜ $+ 2$

2 $1906 = 1000 +$ ⬜ $+ 0 + 6$

3 $2340 = 2000 + 300 + 40 +$ ⬜   ⃝ 3

Write the next two numbers in these lines.

4	8	19	30	41	52	____ ____
5	$4\frac{1}{2}$	7	$9\frac{1}{2}$	12	$14\frac{1}{2}$	____ ____
6	31	27	23	19	15	____ ____
7–8	1	2	3	5	8	____ ____	⃝ 5

9–15 Complete the following sales board.

SALE	
Ordinary price	Half price
£9.80	
£5.20	
	£2.90
£7.40	
	£2.60
£10.20	
	£4.70

7

Underline the numbers which are divisible by 3.

16–18 　69　　　　101　　　　58　　　　405　　　　521　　　　3

19–20 　602　　　　73　　　　237　　　　35　　　　852　　　　484

5

Write the name **semicircle**, **equilateral triangle**, **isosceles triangle**, **quadrilateral**, **pentagon**, **hexagon**, **heptagon**, **cube**, **tetrahedron** or **parallelogram** under the correct shapes.

21
_____

22
_____

23
_____

24
_____

25
_____

26
_____

27
_____

28
_____

29
_____

30
_____

31
_____

32
_____

12

33 Which of the shapes on the page before has the
most edges? _____ 1

34 James weighs 50 kg, which is _____ kg to the nearest 100 kg. 1

35–40 Put these numbers in order, largest to smallest.

3512   2531   3521   1523   2513   1532

_____   _____   _____   _____   _____   _____ 6

Now go to the Progress Chart to record your score!   Total   40

Paper 24

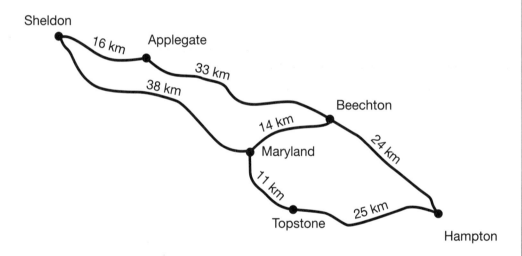

1 From Applegate to Hampton (going through Beechton) is _____ km.

2 From Sheldon to Hampton (going through Maryland and Topstone) is
_____ km.

3–4 The shortest journey from Maryland to Applegate goes through
_____ and is _____ km long.

5–6 The shortest journey from Beechton to Sheldon goes through
_____ and is _____ km long. 6

Look at this calculation carefully and use it to help you with the following questions.

$27 + 21 = 48$

7 $127 + 121 =$ _____

8 $48 - 21 =$ _____

9 $527 + 221 =$ _____

10 $248 - 21 =$ _____

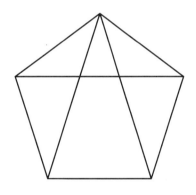

Here is another example and set of questions.

$52 + 16 = 68$

11 $252 + 116 =$ _____

12 $852 + 116 =$ _____

13 $68 - 16 =$ _____

14 $768 - 216 =$ _____

15 What is the name of the outside **polygon**? _____

16 How many **squares** can you find in the polygon? _____

17 What is the name of a polygon with seven sides? _____

Fill in the missing numbers in each line.

18–19 $2\frac{1}{2}$ 4 $5\frac{1}{2}$ 7   _____   _____

20–21 33   _____   39   42   _____   48

22–23 _____   38   34   30   26   _____

24–25 2p   _____   8p   _____   14p   17p

4

4

3

8

Southcross School has 4 half-hour lessons each morning.

26–34 The lessons start at 9:40 and there is a break of 20 minutes after the 2nd lesson. Fill in the timetable.

	Begins	Ends
First lesson	09:40	
Second lesson		
Break		
Third lesson		
Fourth lesson		

9

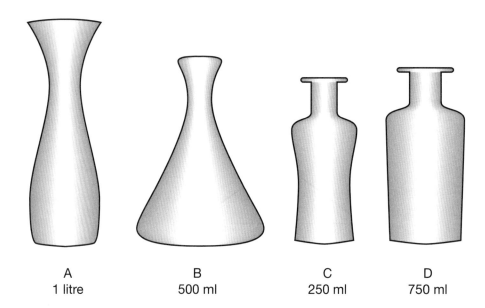

A	B	C	D
1 litre	500 ml	250 ml	750 ml

35 How many times could you fill bottle C from bottle A? _____

36 Bottle A holds twice as much as bottle _____ .

37 Bottle D and bottle _____ together hold as much as A.

38 How much more does A hold than D? _____ ml

39 How many times could you fill C from D? _____

5

40 468 × 7 = _____

1

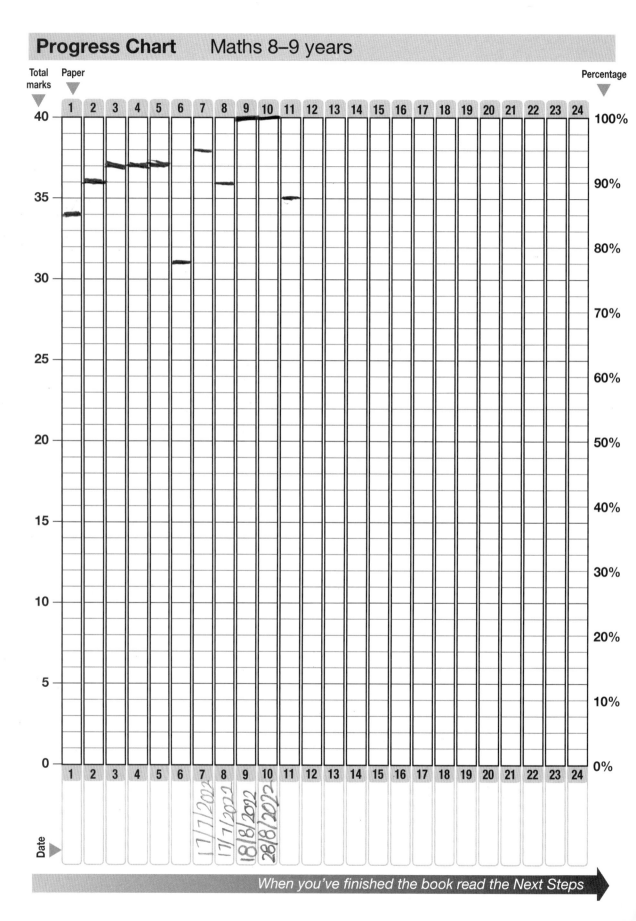